This book belongs to:

Travel Agency:

Email:

ABTA:

ATOL:

Website:

Address:

Postcode:

Notes:

Things to do:

- [ ]
- [ ]
- [ ]
- [ ]
- [ ]
- [ ]
- [ ]
- [ ]
- [ ]
- [ ]
- [ ]
- [ ]
- [ ]
- [ ]
- [ ]
- [ ]
- [ ]
- [ ]
- [ ]
- [ ]

Date:	Ref:
Lead name:	DOB: / /
Preferred dates:	
Number of travellers:	
Names:	DOB: / /
Email address:	Tel:

Preferred destinations:

Accomodation:

Preferred airport(s):

Hold luggage:	Seating:

Budget:	Occasion:

Extras:

Notes:

Dates:	
Airline:	
Flight no:	
Depart:	Depart :
Arrive:	Arrive :
Luggage:	
Notes:	

Accomodation:	Check in:
	Check out:
Extras:	

Flight cost:
Accomodation cost:
Taxes / Extras:
Commission:

Total price:

Price per person:	
Deposit payable to book:	
Remaining:	Due:

Sent: ☐ Follow up: ☐   Booked: ☐ Paid: ☐

Notes:

Notes:

Date:	Ref:
Lead name:	DOB: / /
Preferred dates:	
Number of travellers:	
Names:	DOB: / /
Email address:	Tel:

Preferred destinations:

Accomodation:

Preferred airport(s):

Hold luggage:	Seating:

Budget:	Occasion:

Extras:

Notes:

Dates:	
Airline:	
Flight no:	
Depart:	Depart :
Arrive:	Arrive :
Luggage:	
Notes:	

Accomodation:	Check in:
	Check out:
Extras:	

Flight cost:	
Accomodation cost:	
Taxes / Extras:	
Commission:	

Total price:	

Price per person:	
Deposit payable to book:	
Remaining:	Due:

Sent: ☐ Follow up: ☐ Booked: ☐ Paid: ☐

Notes:

Notes:

Date:	Ref:

Lead name:	DOB: / /
Preferred dates:	
Number of travellers:	
Names:	DOB: / /
Email address:	Tel:

Preferred destinations:	
Accomodation:	
Preferred airport(s):	
Hold luggage:	Seating:
Budget:	Occasion:
Extras:	

Notes:

Dates:	
Airline:	
Flight no:	
Depart:	Depart :
Arrive:	Arrive :
Luggage:	
Notes:	

Accomodation:	Check in:
	Check out:
Extras:	

Flight cost:

Accomodation cost:

Taxes / Extras:

Commission:

Total price:

Price per person:

Deposit payable to book:

Remaining: Due:

Sent: ☐ Follow up: ☐   Booked: ☐ Paid: ☐

Notes:

Notes:

Date:	Ref:
Lead name:	DOB: / /
Preferred dates:	
Number of travellers:	
Names:	DOB: / /
Email address:	Tel:

Preferred destinations:

Accomodation:

Preferred airport(s):

Hold luggage:	Seating:

Budget:	Occasion:

Extras:

Notes:

Dates:	
Airline:	
Flight no:	
Depart:	Depart :
Arrive:	Arrive :
Luggage:	
Notes:	
Accomodation:	Check in:
	Check out:
Extras:	
Flight cost:	
Accomodation cost:	
Taxes / Extras:	
Commission:	
Total price:	
Price per person:	
Deposit payable to book:	
Remaining:	Due:

Sent: ☐   Follow up: ☐   Booked: ☐   Paid: ☐

Notes:

Notes:

Date:	Ref:

Lead name:	DOB: / /

Preferred dates:

Number of travellers:

Names:	DOB: / /

Email address:	Tel:

Preferred destinations:

Accomodation:

Preferred airport(s):

Hold luggage:	Seating:

Budget:	Occasion:

Extras:

Notes:

Dates:	

Airline:	
Flight no:	
Depart:	Depart :
Arrive:	Arrive :
Luggage:	
Notes:	

Accomodation:	Check in:
	Check out:
Extras:	

Flight cost:

Accomodation cost:

Taxes / Extras:

Commission:

Total price:

Price per person:

Deposit payable to book:

Remaining:	Due:

Sent: ☐   Follow up: ☐   Booked: ☐   Paid: ☐

Notes:

Notes:

Date:	Ref:

Lead name:	DOB: / /

Preferred dates:

Number of travellers:

Names:	DOB: / /

Email address:	Tel:

Preferred destinations:

Accomodation:

Preferred airport(s):

Hold luggage:	Seating:

Budget:	Occasion:

Extras:

Notes:

Dates:	
Airline:	
Flight no:	
Depart:	Depart :
Arrive:	Arrive :
Luggage:	
Notes:	

Accomodation:	Check in:
	Check out:
Extras:	

Flight cost:

Accomodation cost:

Taxes / Extras:

Commission:

Total price:

Price per person:

Deposit payable to book:

Remaining: Due:

Sent: ☐   Follow up: ☐   Booked: ☐   Paid: ☐

Notes:

Notes:

Date:	Ref:
Lead name:	DOB: / /
Preferred dates:	
Number of travellers:	
Names:	DOB: / /
Email address:	Tel:

Preferred destinations:

Accomodation:

Preferred airport(s):

Hold luggage:	Seating:
Budget:	Occasion:

Extras:

Notes:

Dates:	
Airline:	
Flight no:	
Depart:	Depart :
Arrive:	Arrive :
Luggage:	
Notes:	
Accomodation:	Check in:
	Check out:
Extras:	
Flight cost:	
Accomodation cost:	
Taxes / Extras:	
Commission:	
Total price:	
Price per person:	
Deposit payable to book:	
Remaining:	Due:

Sent: ☐   Follow up: ☐   Booked: ☐   Paid: ☐

Notes:

Notes:

Date:	Ref:
Lead name:	DOB: / /
Preferred dates:	
Number of travellers:	
Names:	DOB: / /
Email address:	Tel:

Preferred destinations:

Accomodation:

Preferred airport(s):

Hold luggage:	Seating:
Budget:	Occasion:
Extras:	

Notes:

Dates:	
Airline:	
Flight no:	
Depart:	Depart :
Arrive:	Arrive :
Luggage:	
Notes:	

Accomodation:	Check in:
	Check out:
Extras:	

Flight cost:

Accomodation cost:

Taxes / Extras:

Commission:

Total price:

Price per person:

Deposit payable to book:

Remaining: Due:

Sent: ☐ Follow up: ☐ Booked: ☐ Paid: ☐

Notes:

Notes:

Date:	Ref:

Lead name:	DOB: / /

Preferred dates:

Number of travellers:

Names:	DOB: / /

Email address:	Tel:

Preferred destinations:

Accomodation:

Preferred airport(s):

Hold luggage:	Seating:

Budget:	Occasion:

Extras:

Notes:

Dates:	
Airline:	
Flight no:	
Depart:	Depart :
Arrive:	Arrive :
Luggage:	
Notes:	
Accomodation:	Check in:
	Check out:
Extras:	
Flight cost:	
Accomodation cost:	
Taxes / Extras:	
Commission:	
Total price:	
Price per person:	
Deposit payable to book:	
Remaining:	Due:

Sent: ☐   Follow up: ☐   Booked: ☐   Paid: ☐

Notes:

Notes:

Date:	Ref:
Lead name:	DOB: / /
Preferred dates:	
Number of travellers:	
Names:	DOB: / /
Email address:	Tel:

Preferred destinations:
Accomodation:
Preferred airport(s):

Hold luggage:	Seating:
Budget:	Occasion:
Extras:	

Notes:

Dates:	
Airline:	
Flight no:	
Depart:	Depart :
Arrive:	Arrive :
Luggage:	
Notes:	
Accomodation:	Check in:
	Check out:
Extras:	
Flight cost:	
Accomodation cost:	
Taxes / Extras:	
Commission:	
Total price:	
Price per person:	
Deposit payable to book:	
Remaining:	Due:

Sent: ☐ Follow up: ☐   Booked: ☐ Paid: ☐

Notes:

Notes:

Date:	Ref:
Lead name:	DOB: / /

Preferred dates:

Number of travellers:

Names:	DOB: / /

Email address:	Tel:

Preferred destinations:

Accomodation:

Preferred airport(s):

Hold luggage:	Seating:

Budget:	Occasion:

Extras:

Notes:

Dates:

Airline:
Flight no:
Depart: Depart   :
Arrive: Arrive   :
Luggage:
Notes:

Accomodation: Check in:
Check out:
Extras:

Flight cost:
Accomodation cost:
Taxes / Extras:
Commission:

Total price:

Price per person:
Deposit payable to book:
Remaining: Due:

Sent: ☐   Follow up: ☐   Booked: ☐   Paid: ☐

Notes:

Notes:

Date:	Ref:
Lead name:	DOB: / /
Preferred dates:	
Number of travellers:	
Names:	DOB: / /
Email address:	Tel:

Preferred destinations:

Accomodation:

Preferred airport(s):

Hold luggage:	Seating:
Budget:	Occasion:

Extras:

Notes:

Dates:	
Airline:	
Flight no:	
Depart:	Depart :
Arrive:	Arrive :
Luggage:	
Notes:	

Accomodation:	Check in:
	Check out:
Extras:	

Flight cost:

Accomodation cost:

Taxes / Extras:

Commission:

Total price:

Price per person:

Deposit payable to book:

Remaining: Due:

Sent: ☐   Follow up: ☐   Booked: ☐   Paid: ☐

Notes:

Notes:

Date:	Ref:

Lead name:	DOB: / /

Preferred dates:

Number of travellers:

Names:	DOB: / /

Email address:	Tel:

Preferred destinations:

Accomodation:

Preferred airport(s):

Hold luggage:	Seating:

Budget:	Occasion:

Extras:

Notes:

Dates:	
Airline:	
Flight no:	
Depart:	Depart :
Arrive:	Arrive :
Luggage:	
Notes:	

Accomodation:	Check in:
	Check out:
Extras:	

Flight cost:
Accomodation cost:
Taxes / Extras:
Commission:

Total price:

Price per person:
Deposit payable to book:
Remaining: Due:

Sent: ☐   Follow up: ☐   Booked: ☐   Paid: ☐

Notes:

Notes:

Date:	Ref:

Lead name:	DOB: / /

Preferred dates:

Number of travellers:

Names:	DOB: / /

Email address:	Tel:

Preferred destinations:

Accomodation:

Preferred airport(s):

Hold luggage:	Seating:

Budget:	Occasion:

Extras:

Notes:

Dates:	
Airline:	
Flight no:	
Depart:	Depart :
Arrive:	Arrive :
Luggage:	
Notes:	

Accomodation:	Check in:
	Check out:
Extras:	

Flight cost:

Accomodation cost:

Taxes / Extras:

Commission:

Total price:

Price per person:

Deposit payable to book:

Remaining: Due:

Sent: ☐ Follow up: ☐ Booked: ☐ Paid: ☐

Notes:

Notes:

Date:	Ref:

Lead name:	DOB: / /
Preferred dates:	
Number of travellers:	
Names:	DOB: / /
Email address:	Tel:

Preferred destinations:

Accomodation:

Preferred airport(s):

Hold luggage:	Seating:

Budget:	Occasion:

Extras:

Notes:

Dates:	

Airline:	
Flight no:	
Depart:	Depart :
Arrive:	Arrive :
Luggage:	
Notes:	

Accomodation:	Check in:
	Check out:
Extras:	

Flight cost:
Accomodation cost:
Taxes / Extras:
Commission:

Total price:

Price per person:	
Deposit payable to book:	
Remaining:	Due:

Sent: ☐   Follow up: ☐   Booked: ☐   Paid: ☐

Notes:

Notes:

Date:	Ref:
Lead name:	DOB: / /
Preferred dates:	
Number of travellers:	
Names:	DOB: / /
Email address:	Tel:

Preferred destinations:

Accomodation:

Preferred airport(s):

Hold luggage:	Seating:
Budget:	Occasion:

Extras:

Notes:

Dates:

| Airline: |
| Flight no: |
| Depart: | Depart : |
| Arrive: | Arrive : |
| Luggage: |
| Notes: |

| Accomodation: | Check in: |
| | Check out: |
| Extras: |

| Flight cost: |
| Accomodation cost: |
| Taxes / Extras: |
| Commission: |
| Total price: |
| Price per person: |
| Deposit payable to book: |
| Remaining: | Due: |
| Sent: ☐ Follow up: ☐ | Booked: ☐ Paid: ☐ |

Notes:

Notes:

Date:	Ref:

Lead name:	DOB: / /

Preferred dates:

Number of travellers:

Names:	DOB: / /

Email address:	Tel:

Preferred destinations:

Accomodation:

Preferred airport(s):

Hold luggage:	Seating:

Budget:	Occasion:

Extras:

Notes:

Dates:

Airline:	
Flight no:	
Depart:	Depart :
Arrive:	Arrive :
Luggage:	
Notes:	

Accomodation:	Check in:
	Check out:
Extras:	

Flight cost:
Accomodation cost:
Taxes / Extras:
Commission:

Total price:

Price per person:	
Deposit payable to book:	
Remaining:	Due:

Sent: ☐   Follow up: ☐   Booked: ☐   Paid: ☐

Notes:

Notes:

Date:	Ref:

Lead name:	DOB: / /
Preferred dates:	
Number of travellers:	
Names:	DOB: / /
Email address:	Tel:

Preferred destinations:

Accomodation:

Preferred airport(s):

Hold luggage:	Seating:
Budget:	Occasion:
Extras:	

Notes:

Dates:	
Airline:	
Flight no:	
Depart:	Depart :
Arrive:	Arrive :
Luggage:	
Notes:	
Accomodation:	Check in:
	Check out:
Extras:	
Flight cost:	
Accomodation cost:	
Taxes / Extras:	
Commission:	
Total price:	
Price per person:	
Deposit payable to book:	
Remaining:	Due:

Sent: ☐ Follow up: ☐   Booked: ☐ Paid: ☐

Notes:

Notes:

Date:	Ref:

Lead name:	DOB: / /

Preferred dates:

Number of travellers:

Names:	DOB: / /

Email address:	Tel:

Preferred destinations:

Accomodation:

Preferred airport(s):

Hold luggage:	Seating:

Budget:	Occasion:

Extras:

Notes:

Dates:	
Airline:	
Flight no:	
Depart:	Depart :
Arrive:	Arrive :
Luggage:	
Notes:	

Accomodation:	Check in:
	Check out:
Extras:	

Flight cost:	
Accomodation cost:	
Taxes / Extras:	
Commission:	

Total price:	

Price per person:	
Deposit payable to book:	
Remaining:	Due:

Sent: ☐   Follow up: ☐   Booked: ☐   Paid: ☐

Notes:

Notes:

Date:	Ref:
Lead name:	DOB: / /
Preferred dates:	
Number of travellers:	
Names:	DOB: / /
Email address:	Tel:

Preferred destinations:

Accomodation:

Preferred airport(s):

Hold luggage:	Seating:
Budget:	Occasion:

Extras:

Notes:

Dates:	

Airline:	
Flight no:	
Depart:	Depart :
Arrive:	Arrive :
Luggage:	
Notes:	

Accomodation:	Check in:
	Check out:
Extras:	

Flight cost:
Accomodation cost:
Taxes / Extras:
Commission:

Total price:

Price per person:	
Deposit payable to book:	
Remaining:	Due:

Sent: ☐   Follow up: ☐   Booked: ☐   Paid: ☐

Notes:

Notes:

Date:	Ref:

Lead name:	DOB: / /

Preferred dates:

Number of travellers:

Names:	DOB: / /

Email address:	Tel:

Preferred destinations:

Accomodation:

Preferred airport(s):

Hold luggage:	Seating:

Budget:	Occasion:

Extras:

Notes:

Dates:	
Airline:	
Flight no:	
Depart:	Depart :
Arrive:	Arrive :
Luggage:	
Notes:	

Accomodation:	Check in:
	Check out:
Extras:	

Flight cost:	
Accomodation cost:	
Taxes / Extras:	
Commission:	
Total price:	

Price per person:	
Deposit payable to book:	
Remaining:	Due:

Sent: ☐   Follow up: ☐   Booked: ☐   Paid: ☐

Notes:

Notes:

Date:	Ref:

Lead name:	DOB: / /

Preferred dates:

Number of travellers:

Names:	DOB: / /

Email address:	Tel:

Preferred destinations:

Accomodation:

Preferred airport(s):

Hold luggage:	Seating:

Budget:	Occasion:

Extras:

Notes:

Dates:	
Airline:	
Flight no:	
Depart:	Depart :
Arrive:	Arrive :
Luggage:	
Notes:	

Accomodation:	Check in:
	Check out:
Extras:	

Flight cost:
Accomodation cost:
Taxes / Extras:
Commission:

Total price:

Price per person:	
Deposit payable to book:	
Remaining:	Due:

Sent: ☐   Follow up: ☐   Booked: ☐   Paid: ☐

Notes:

Notes:

Things to do:

- [ ]
- [ ]
- [ ]
- [ ]
- [ ]
- [ ]
- [ ]
- [ ]
- [ ]
- [ ]
- [ ]
- [ ]
- [ ]
- [ ]
- [ ]
- [ ]
- [ ]
- [ ]
- [ ]
- [ ]

Things to do:

- [ ]
- [ ]
- [ ]
- [ ]
- [ ]
- [ ]
- [ ]
- [ ]
- [ ]
- [ ]
- [ ]
- [ ]
- [ ]
- [ ]
- [ ]
- [ ]
- [ ]
- [ ]
- [ ]
- [ ]

- [ ]
- [ ]
- [ ]
- [ ]
- [ ]
- [ ]
- [ ]
- [ ]
- [ ]
- [ ]
- [ ]
- [ ]
- [ ]
- [ ]
- [ ]
- [ ]
- [ ]
- [ ]
- [ ]
- [ ]

Things to do:

- [ ]
- [ ]
- [ ]
- [ ]
- [ ]
- [ ]
- [ ]
- [ ]
- [ ]
- [ ]
- [ ]
- [ ]
- [ ]
- [ ]
- [ ]
- [ ]
- [ ]
- [ ]
- [ ]
- [ ]

Things to do:

- [ ]   [ ]
- [ ]   [ ]
- [ ]   [ ]
- [ ]   [ ]
- [ ]   [ ]
- [ ]   [ ]
- [ ]   [ ]
- [ ]   [ ]
- [ ]   [ ]
- [ ]   [ ]
- [ ]   [ ]
- [ ]   [ ]
- [ ]   [ ]
- [ ]   [ ]
- [ ]   [ ]
- [ ]   [ ]
- [ ]   [ ]
- [ ]   [ ]
- [ ]   [ ]
- [ ]   [ ]

Notes: